365
Ways to
Pamper Yourself

365 Ways to Pamper Yourself

Magpie Books, London

Constable & Robinson Ltd
3 The Lanchesters
162 Fulham Palace Road
London W6 9ER
www.constablerobinson.com

This edition published by Magpie Books,
an imprint of Constable & Robinson Ltd 2005

ISBN 1 84529 196 4

A copy of the British Library Cataloguing in Publications Data is available from the British Library

Printed and bound in the EU

1

Give yourself permission to do something special for yourself, at least once a week. Maybe you want to spend an hour listening to music, reading a book or taking a bubble bath with scented candles burning.

2

Sit outside in the garden as evening comes. This is a magical time of day and something that should definitely be experienced. Listen to how the birds sing as the sun sets. Some flowers have a stronger fragrance in the evening and your garden may well smell differently from how it does in the day.

3

A great lifting face-mask

1 tablespoon almonds
1 tablespoon honey
1 egg white

Grind the almonds into a fine meal in a blender or food processor. Mix the almond meal together with the honey and the egg white. Apply to face and let set for about 15 minutes. Gently wipe off with a damp washcloth.

4

Place dried camomile, rosemary, lavender and lemon balm in small cloth bags. Place the bags in a bathroom, under cushions or other places where pressure or warmth will release a wonderful smell.

5

Decide you're going to have a makeover and get a new hairstyle.

6

Energy-booster bath

½ cup sea salt
½ cup baking powder
1 teaspoon sunflower oil
2 to 3 drops rosemary essential oil

Bath salts are invigorating when used as a body scrub or added to the tub. They open pores, allowing the skin to absorb healing trace minerals and vitamins. Rosemary essential oil stimulates circulation and clears the mind. Place all ingredients in a plastic bag (such as a freezer-bag) and knead until well mixed. Add one to two tablespoons to running bath water or use as a scrub on your body.

7

Take one evening just to pamper yourself

Have a relaxing bath and body soak and give yourself a manicure and pedicure. You can then polish your nails using your favorite polish. This treatment will make your finger- and toenails look more attractive, it will also make you feel more attractive on the inside. A great boost for your self-esteem.

8

Petting animals lowers blood pressure and makes you feel more peaceful and therefore will benefit you. If you don't have a pet, find a petting zoo and play with the animals.

9

Make yourself a steaming cup of tea, hot chocolate, or flavoured coffee. Camomile tea is a relaxing choice, while mint teas are a natural pick-me-up. Hot chocolate is a low-fat way to satisfy a sweet tooth, as are flavoured coffees such as mocha or French vanilla.

10

To deep-cleanse oily skin

½ a peeled, sliced cucumber puréed
1 tablespoon yoghurt

Apply to face and allow to set for about 20 minutes. Gently wipe off with a damp washcloth.

11

Look after your hair

Don't brush your hair while it is still wet. Use a wide-toothed comb to comb through your hair. Wait till your hair is about 75 per cent dry before you start to blow-dry.

12

Learn how to do simple deep-breathing exercises and fill your body with oxygen. When you are stressed or tense, your muscles tighten, and you do not breathe as deeply as you normally would.
Be sure to sit up straight and expand your lungs. Breathe in through your nose and exhale through your mouth. Hold your breath for a few seconds before exhaling.

13

To detox the skin

Create a salt bath oil using sea salt and sweet almond oil. Patchouli and lemongrass essential oil can be added if you like the smell. This will help to clean and soften the skin. Use a detox bath for two days in a row to give yourself glowing skin ready for your holidays.

14

Take one whole day off and be totally alone. During your free day, do only what you want to do.

15

Home-made facial scrub

2 tablespoons oatmeal
1 teaspoon ground almonds
1 teaspoon apple cider vinegar
1 teaspoon spring water in bowl

Indulge your face with this great home-made facial scrub for normal/oily skin. Mix the ingredients into a paste with a crumbly consistency. If the paste is too thick, add more water. Using an upward motion, work into the skin. The oatmeal will fall off your face, leaving behind a film. Allow the film to penetrate for 15–20 minutes or until it hardens. Take a dry washcloth and buff. The film will flake off, taking the dead skin with it.

16

Spend some money or save some, just for you. Even something small can make you feel special and powerful.

17

Have your own spa party at home. Invite your friends round. Stock up on beauty products or get everyone to bring something. Indulge yourselves in an evening of pampering.

18

Think of one luxury you would love to indulge yourself with. Start planning on having it by taking tiny steps toward getting it. No matter how extravagant it is you will always be a little bit closer.

19

Smooth your cuticles and pamper your nails

Papaya contains a natural enzyme which helps dissolve dead skin. Mash two papayas with a fork and work into your cuticles (avocado and lemon may be substituted for papaya). Rinse off. Apply olive oil, canola oil or sweet almond oil to soften the cuticle beds. Use twice a week.

✤ ✤ ✤

20

Get a new film in your camera and go for a long walk outdoors. Look for unusual sights and photograph them.

21

Keep products by your shower to cater for various moods

Try jasmine and rose oil on your shower sponge to relax. Citrus and ginger oils will get you energized.

22

To give your hands an extra treat use your night-cream on them once a week before you go to sleep.

23

Go out for breakfast. It might be to the little cafe close by, or somewhere you always wanted to visit.

24

Hide from people

Sometimes you just need to hide to relax and re-energize yourself.

25

Have a nap!

There's no bad time for a nap. You don't have to actually go to sleep. Just stretch out on the couch and relax. Think pleasant thoughts and banish bad ones.

26

Dry-brush your body three days a week for a month to get rid of dead skin cells. Dry-brushing your skin will help your body to glow and will also boost your circulation, which helps to fight cellulite.

27

Forget the diet for once and have a treat. Make a delicious dessert and eat it in bed or lounging on the sofa.

28

Give yourself a scalp massage

1. Stroke your fingertips along the scalp from the forehead to the back of the head, then from the sides of the head to the top.
2. Brace your thumbs near the top or back of the head. Rotate your fingertips in small circles on the scalp.
3. Brace your thumbs on the sides of the head and rotate your fingertips in small circles on the scalp.
4. Massage the hairline, using fingertips or thumbs, around the ears and across the back of the neck.
5. Brace your fingertips near the temples and place your thumbs at the middle of the hairline just above the forehead.
6. Place one thumb on top of the other and gently circle the thumbs into the scalp.
7. Lift the thumbs and place them an inch back toward the top of the head.

29

Eliminate rushing for one day

Avoid crisis mode! Have a day where you allow plenty of time for everything. For example, arrive 15 minutes early for every appointment. Slowing down, doing less and taking care of yourself physically will actually give you more energy.

30

A night indoors just pampering yourself is good. Bubble baths with candlelight, a facial and a manicure, all with some soft music in the background, are very nice.

31

Keep up appearances

Treat yourself to a manicure twice a month. Or, take your nicest feature (hair, nails, eyes, lips, legs), and make the most of it in a pampering session every month or so.

32

Have a soak to soothe away the day

1 whole egg
2 tablespoons honey
½ cup baby or mineral oil
¼ cup whole fresh milk
2 teaspoons liquid soap or dishwashing liquid
¼ cup fragrant oil (optional)

Mix all the ingredients in a blender for 30 seconds. Use one or two tablespoons of this oil in a bathtub of water.

33

Fine wine, great music

Indulge yourself by buying a great bottle of wine and then sip it while listening to your favourite music.

34

Have a handful of almonds and low-fat yoghurt for your mid-afternoon snack. These carbohydrates should give you energy until dinner.

35

Light a lavender candle or spray a lavender-scented mist when you need a boost. Lavender helps to create a calming and uplifting effect.

36

Soak stress away out of your feet

Fill a tub or footbath with warm water and drop in a ½ ounce of your favourite bath salts (sea salt is a good substitute if you don't have bath salts to hand). Add a tablespoon of olive oil and soak your feet for 10 to 15 minutes. The salts soften up dry skin and calluses and the olive oil moisturizes them.

37

Begin looking after yourself

Start your day with a healthy breakfast. Eating breakfast improves your concentration and your eating habits throughout the day will be healthier.

38

Indulge your curiosity with a local cultural expedition, to a museum or art gallery.

39

it moving in the fresh air. You could go cycling, running, hiking, trekking or walking.

40

An oatmeal-based face-mask to cleanse and tone your skin

1 small pot natural yoghurt
1 teaspoon lavender oil
a handful of oatmeal

Mix the lavender oil and the yoghurt in a bowl, then stir in the oatmeal until the mixture has the consistency of a paste. Spread the mixture over your face, avoiding the eyes and mouth. Lie down and relax for about ten minutes to allow the mask to tighten. Remove the mask by rinsing your face with tepid water.

41

If it's summer try sleeping in the garden under the stars. It is wonderfully peaceful.

42

cIncite a happy mood in yourself. Compile a list of things your children have said that make you laugh. Keep it in the kitchen or somewhere handy so it's always there to add to, and to read.

43

Find out what you're good at and do it. Our self-esteem increases as our skills are acknowledged. Tell yourself that you deserve all the praise that comes your way.

44

A rose-scented skin toner

3 ½ cups witch hazel
½ cup dried rose petals
5 sprigs of fresh rosemary

Mix ingredients together and blend well. Strain. Splash on your face after washing.

45

Sleep in late

Ignore the alarm clock for once. Naughty, but it does have the feeling of taking back a little power in your life.

46

If you're always busy, be kind to yourself and make lists. Jot everything you have to do on a piece of paper. Do one job at a time. Don't keep thinking about the next job or you'll feel that you're running out of time.

47

If your job is getting you down, get a manicure, pedicure, massage or facial in your lunch hour.

48

Stop grinning and bearing it

Redefine yourself and raise your standards. If you choose to no longer put up with things, you have more energy and time to focus on the things that matter.

49

If you are troubled with greasy hair, shampoo your hair once a month with washing-up liquid. It will make your hair "squeaky" clean by dissolving the build-up of grease and grime.

50

Food rich in beta-carotene can be a cause of red skin. This includes dark-coloured fruit and vegetables, such as carrots, butternut, sweet potatoes, tomatoes, watermelon, papaya, broccoli and spinach. If red patches on your skin are a problem for you, take care not to eat too much of these foods.

51

If you get really tired, take a nap. You will feel better afterwards, but remember that it takes at least 20 minutes to wake up after a 15-minute nap.

52

If you feel stuck in a routine make a deliberate attempt to choose something different. Whether you eat something new for lunch or exercise on the bike instead of watching television, a habit of trying new things will help remind you that life presents a lot of options.

53

Moisturizer for soft skin

1 cup dried camomile
4 tablespoons honey
1 cup milk
8 teaspoons wheatgerm

Steep the camomile in milk for a few hours. Strain and retain the liquid. Add the honey and wheatgerm and blend well. Place in a bottle. Refrigerated, it will keep for up to one week.

54

Boost your self-image by giving your hair some natural highlights. To lighten hair, wet it, add lemon juice and go out into the sun to let it dry naturally.

55

Walking is an excellent tonic for body, mind and spirit. As you walk, fill your senses with the scents, sights and sounds around you. Look at the trees, listen to the birds, feel the breeze and smell the flowers.

56

Home-made herbal body wrap

1 cup of your favourite type of herb or combination of herbs
2 or 3 large beach towels or cotton sheets
Plastic tarp or shower curtain
Large bucket of very hot (not boiling) water

Pamper your body with this do-it-yourself herbal body wrap. Pour your herbs into the water and allow them to soak for five minutes. Add the beach towel or sheets. Lay the plastic tarp or shower curtain on your bed. Wring out the towel or sheets and wrap your body. Lie down on the bed and have someone wrap you in the plastic tarp or shower curtain, then cover yourself with blankets. Lie quietly for no longer than ten minutes. Slowly unwrap yourself and get up.

57

Make a "thankful" list to count your blessings. Make a point to add to the list daily and so keep you aware of the good things in your life.

58

Expand your areas of interest. Take up a hobby like painting, dancing or horse-riding. Once you get into your new hobby you will be able to forget about your worries for a while.

59

A home-made calming flour mask

⅓ cup of wholewheat flour mixed with enough milk to form a paste

Soothe your face with this calming flour mask. Apply the paste to the face and leave it on for 15–20 minutes. Remove with warm water. You can store the excess for a maximum of three days in the refrigerator.

60

Get rid of product build-up on your hair

Once a week, wash your hair thoroughly. When you are about to apply the second squeeze of shampoo, take a tablespoon of baking soda and mix it with the shampoo in your hand. Then wash it for the second time. This works safely on build-up from styling products.

61

Do voluntary work at an animal shelter or work with underprivileged children – it will make you realize how much you have to be thankful for and you will be kinder to yourself.

62

Break away for a weekend and do whatever you like to do best. You can do this either at home or on a short trip away.

63

Yoghurt and honey face-mask

1 teaspoon honey
1 capsule of vitamin A (10,000 iu)
1 tablespoon yoghurt
¾ egg yolk

On cold days try this yoghurt and honey face-mask to deeply moisturize your skin, particularly during winter. Mix everything together. To thicken, add a small amount of cornstarch. Apply the mask to clean skin and leave it on for 20 minutes. Rinse with lukewarm water.

64

Give yourself a quick fashion makeover. Decide the previous evening on something fabulous to wear to work the next day, including accessories. This will save you a lot of time.

65

Thigh-slimming exercise

This will help to strengthen your inner and outer thighs. Use an exercise mat when performing this exercise. Lie on your back, arms at your sides with palms down against the mat and your legs together. Inhale.

Now exhale and pull your stomach up and in toward your spine (to help stabilize your lower back). Bring your right knee to your chest and then raise the leg in the air, at a 90-degree angle to the floor. Try to keep your leg as straight as possible but if you can't keep your raised leg straight, bend the knee a little.

Rotate your raised leg slightly so that your toes point away from the right side of your body. Keep your back, especially the backs of your hips, pressed to the floor. Make about ten small circles in the air (in a clockwise direction) with your right foot.

Now do ten circles in the opposite direction.

Bring your right knee back to your chest and then to the floor. Repeat this exercise with your left leg.

66

Get your friends round and stage your own film festival with rented videos or DVDs.

67

Relaxing bath

1 cup honey
2 cups milk
1 cup salt
¼ cup baking soda
½ cup baby oil
a few drops of the fragrant oil of your choice

If the day has got you down, have a long relaxing bath with this home-made mixture. Combine the honey, milk, salt and baking soda in a bowl. Fill the tub and pour the mixture in. Add the baby oil and a few drops of the fragrance.

68

Facial scrub for oily skin

2 tablespoons of raw bran or oatmeal
2 tablespoons hot water

Cleanse and purify oily skin with this facial scrub. Blend the raw bran or oatmeal with the hot water to make a paste. Scrub the skin for at least two minutes before rinsing off with tepid water.

69

Buy yourself a fabulous pair of sunglasses. They will keep the UV rays out of your eyes and make you feel beautiful every time you catch sight of yourself in shop windows.

70

Bottom-toning exercise

Try this exercise for toning and shaping your bottom.

Stand with your feet shoulder-width apart, your back straight and your shoulders relaxed.

Tighten your buttocks and breathe in and push your hips forward. Hold for ten seconds.

After ten seconds, release the tension in your buttocks and breathe out. Do 20 to 30 repetitions of this exercise.

71

If you have blemishes and impurities on your skin, treat them with crushed garlic.

72

Natural mineral water face-mask

Treat your skin tenderly with this natural mineral water mask to purify it. Select a quality mineral water and pour it into a plastic spray bottle. Add some rose water or camomile. Keep it chilled in the fridge and use it to moisturize and refresh the face on hot days or after exercise.

73

Dry skin treatment

2 tablespoons cornflour
1 teaspoon honey
a few drops of strong camomile tea (cooled)

Look after your body and show it some respect. Wherever your skin is dry, scrub it with this natural sugar made by mixing together the cornflour, the honey and the camomile tea.

74

Decide to turn your life around. Resolve to quit bad habits that can make you feel guilty or depressed, like smoking or overeating.

75

Skin-tightening mask

2–3 egg whites

If your cares and worries have left your face sagging, use egg whites as a skin-tightening mask. Whisk together the egg whites and apply to the face. Allow to dry for about 10–15 minutes then rinse off with warm water.

76

Insomnia remedy

10 drops camomile oil
5 drops clary sage oil
5 drops bergamot oil

Fight insomnia with this mixture of essential oils. Blend the oils and store the mixture in a clean glass bottle. Add one to two drops to a tissue and place inside your pillowcase to help you fall fast asleep.

77

Distance yourself from people who constantly criticize you and put you down; rather hang out with people who make you feel good about yourself when you are around them.

78

Feel civilized, have a special teatime. Take out the good china and have a cup of tea and some cake.

79

Keep organic ingredients around the home to pamper yourself with. Here is a list of natural ingredients to pamper your hair.

To replenish and enrich:
avocado
rose oil
grapeseed oil
olive oil
plum
pumpkin
apricot

To refresh and renew:
cucumber
lemon
lime juice
grapefruit
peppermint
rosemary oil
lavender

80

Smooth your skin

2 tablespoons olive oil
2 tablespoons salt

Mix the olive oil and the salt. Cleanse your face, and hold warm, wet towels on the face for a few minutes to open the pores. Apply the mixture with a circular motion and leave it on for five minutes. Use the same procedure to smooth the backs of your hands and your feet. Rinse off with warm water, and your skin will be clean and smooth.

81

Ear massage

Massage your ears for a quick destress exercise. Gently rub the lobes of your ears between your thumbs and index fingers then gently pull and stroke, working all along the ear. This can be done anywhere: at work, at home or as you travel.

82

Home-made creamy avocado and honey face-mask

2 tablespoons avocado, mashed
3 tablespoons honey
1 egg, separated

Indulge your face with this home-made creamy avocado and honey mask. Mix together the egg yolk, oil and honey. Stir thoroughly. Now add the egg white. Close the container and shake well before applying the face-mask. Leave it on for 15 minutes, then rinse off with warm water.

83

When you treat yourself well and pamper yourself, you are more likely to find that you want to treat your body well with healthier eating and exercise. Pampering yourself is a great way to start a whole process of self-improvement.

84

Mood-enhancing bath

¼ cup grated lemon peel
¼ cup grated orange peel

Lift your spirits at the end of the day with this mood-enhancer: a bath with uplifting citrus scents. Add the grated peel to warm, running bath water.

85

Facial massage

Stroke the sides of your nose with your fingertips, pressing on the area around your nostrils to stimulate the blood flow. Follow the shape of your lips, sliding your hands from the centre towards the outer corners of your upper lip. Apply pressure just above the centre of your upper lip while counting 30, then start on your lower lip massaging upwards in small circles, lifting and encircling your mouth.

86

Always have some of your favourite chocolates or goodies in the house. There will always be times when you deserve them.

87

Mood-enhancing essential oils

Essential oils can encourage positive moods. Citrus oils tend to be energizing while floral oils are good for stress relief. Lavender oil is very relaxing and is also said to have a soothing effect on cuts, bruises and insect bites. Peppermint oil has been known to increase mental alertness, and rosemary is reputed to be invigorating for low-energy days.

88

Have a bath to relax and refresh you, whether you have ten minutes or an hour. A bath should not only cleanse you, but should also soothe and calm you and banish weariness.

89

Give your sense of duty and obligations a makeover. Learn to say "no" when the answer should be "no", and you will give yourself lots more free time to pamper yourself.

90

Home-made herbal soap

1½ cups of herbs (lavender, mint, rose petals, bee balm – choose your favourite)
essential oil (of the herb of your choice)
1½ quarts of water
2 cups shredded, pure soap
½ cup borax

Make your own soft, herbal soap – free of additives and harsh perfumes. Boil the herbs in a saucepan (an enamel one, preferably) and simmer for 30 minutes to release the oils. Stir in the soap and the borax. Boil gently for three minutes and cool. Add a few drops of the essential oil and pour the mixture into covered containers.

91

For great hair you need vitamins. Be sure to take your B vitamins – B6, B12 and folic acid are associated with moisture-rich hair. You can take a multivitamin or eat foods rich in B vitamins including soya beans, bananas, beans, yoghurt, avocados, eggs and grains.

92

Ask your best friends for a list of their all-time favourite movies. Take their suggestions to the video rental store and plan a movie night in with some beer or a good wine and popcorn.

93

Massage your forehead to relieve stress. Place some moisturizing cream on the pad of your middle finger and massage upwards in small clockwise circles from the centre of your forehead, sliding your fingers along your hairline. Finish up by applying gentle pressure at your temples while slowly counting to 30. Repeat three times.

94

Bath salts

1 cup salt
1 cup Epsom salts
1 cup baking soda
1 cup shampoo (optional)
a few drops of essential oil (optional)

If you feel tired, make some energizing bath salts by mixing together the above ingredients and allow yourself a good soak. Add a little of the mixture to your tub for a revitalizing bath. For bubbles, just add one cup of shampoo. For a nice scent, add a few drops of an essential oil.

95

If it's cold, wrap yourself in warm clothing and go for a brisk walk. Just 30 minutes of walking in the fresh air will leave your face glowing. In summer enjoy the feeling of warm sunlight on your skin.

96

Scented hair

2 drops of rosemary, lavender or sandalwood essential oil

Apply two drops of the essential oil of your choice to the bristles of your hairbrush and brush your hair thoroughly. The oils will leave your hair shining and smelling wonderful.

97

Turn your bed into an ultra-comfort zone with fresh sheets and a few drops of lavender oil to help you to relax and get to sleep.

98

Have a session to take care of your nails. Store your nail polish in the fridge to make it last longer, but let it reach room temperature before applying. Wipe your nail polish bottle lid with nail polish remover after you've used it and secure it tightly after use to prevent it from thickening and to make it easy to open the next time you use it.

99

Organic, detoxifying face cleanser

1 cup red raspberries (crushed with juice)
1 tablespoon sea salt
1 pot of organic natural yoghurt

Use this great organic face cleanser to detox your skin. Mix the ingredients together in a bowl with a mixer or in a blender until creamy. Then place in a microwave for about 30 seconds, or heat on the stove until very warm to the touch (stir so that the mixture doesn't stick or burn). Allow to cool. Apply to face with an upward, circular motion. Rinse with warm water. Store the remaining mixture in airtight container in the refrigerator. It will keep for up to ten days.

100

Bruise balm

1 ounce of sweet almond oil
8 drops of arnica

Treat bruises with this home-made bruise balm. Mix the arnica into the sweet almond oil. Apply the mixture lightly to bruises once or twice a day.

101

If possible, put up a hammock in your garden and gently rock away the afternoon. If there's no place for a hammock, invest in a reclining chair and rest in that instead.

102

Go for a walk in the evening after the sun has gone down on a bright day. Watch the colours of the sunset. After the sun has gone below the horizon, look at the stars.

103

Camomile skin spritzer

3 camomile teabags
spring water

Boil the spring water and add the teabags. Continue boiling for five minutes. Allow to cool. Pour the liquid into a spray bottle and store it in the fridge. Shake before use and use as a toner or a spritzer on a hot day – it is soothing, anti-inflammatory and smells wonderful. The spritzer will keep for up to 14 days in the fridge.

104

Have a "good grooming" day where you give yourself a pedicure, wax your legs and pluck your eyebrows.

105

Start now to do some some exercise. Exercising makes you feel leaner and healthier. It will also make you feel happy and more energetic and nothing is sexier than someone who feels good about himself or herself.

106

If you have oily or acne-prone skin, a great pampering treatment is to use coarse sea salt as a facial scrub.

107

Go for a long walk somewhere you know you will find lots of wild flowers. Spend some time looking at them and admiring their beauty.

108

Lip balm

1 teaspoon turmeric
1 teaspoon nutmeg
1 teaspoon butter

Try this quick remedy for chapped lips. Mix together equal amounts of turmeric, nutmeg and fresh butter and apply to sore, dry lips.

109

Once a week, or every other week, get your hair done at the hairdresser's. A haircut and some highlights can alter your appearance and stop you feeling dull.

110

"Make sure you are treated well by others. No one can make you feel inferior without your permission."

Eleanor Roosevelt

111

You are special

Remember times when you were fully in control and doing well. Relive those moments so you can use them as triggering mechanisms when you are feeling low.

112

Fresh pineapple and coconut shake

¾ cup diced pineapple
1 medium banana, diced
2 tablespoons low-fat coconut milk
⅓ cup non-fat plain yoghurt

Indulge your taste buds with this fresh pineapple and coconut shake. Combine all the ingredients in a blender and purée. Makes a single 12-ounce shake.

113

Cheer yourself up

Watch a comedy video or go to a comedy club and see what you find the most amusing. The chances are that things you find the most funny are somehow related to how you see yourself.

114

Early in the morning, just before the sun has risen, go for a walk in the moonlight. At dawn sit down and watch the sunrise.

115

Have your hair cut, coloured or styled in your lunch hour to brighten up a dull working day.

116

Make any evening a special evening by going out for dinner with your partner or a good friend.

117

Skin-nourishing mask

2 tablespoons honey
3 tablespoons olive oil or mineral oil
1 whole egg, separated

If you feel a bit tired try this skin-nourishing mask. Mix together the egg yolk, the oil and the honey. Stir thoroughly. Now add the egg white. Close the container and shake well before applying.

118

To make the most of bath time, invest in an air-filled adjustable pillow so you can just lie back and enjoy a long comfortable soak.

119

Make your life happier by identifying your priorities and committing yourself to them. Banish anything that gets in the way of living by your priorities.

120

Apply body moisturizer after your bath. Use a product that will not only soften your skin, but that also contains a unique light-diffusion system to ensure a healthy glow. Even better, chose one that contains your favourite scent.

121

There should be someone in your life you can depend on to pamper, heal and revitalize you. Why can that "someone" not be you? Think of something that would bring you great pleasure. Then give it to yourself.

122

Here's a great, quick way to revitalize your skin. Splash your face with warm, clean water to open your pores. Apply either a mask or a gentle exfoliating scrub. Lie down for a few minutes before you rinse your face with clean water.

123

Buttermilk mask

⅓ cup rolled oats
1 carton buttermilk
1 capsule vitamin A (10,000 iu)

Soothe your skin with this home-made buttermilk mask (particularly any dry skin areas). Soak the rolled oats in the buttermilk. Strain. Add the vitamin A and mix well. After cleansing the skin, apply the mixture and leave it on for 10–15 minutes. Rinse off with tepid water.

124

Light some candles in your favourite room in the house and enjoy the candlelight alone for at least 15 minutes.

125

Eliminate redundant activities

Give yourself more time by eliminating redundant activities. Banish anything in your life that does not contribute to your personal or professional development. This will free up valuable time for more enjoyable activities.

126

Value your time

Don't let others invade your own special "me" time with unnecessary interruptions or long conversations. If you value your time, others will.

127

Go and lose yourself in a film once a week. You could go alone or with a friend.

128

Skin-balancing oatmeal-honey face-mask

½ cup uncooked oatmeal
3 tablespoons honey
1 egg yolk

Relax with this skin-balancing oatmeal-honey face mask. Mix all the ingredients together and apply over the entire face. Masssage in a circular motion. Leave on for ten minutes.

129

Organize your mental space

Resolve personal issues and issues that hold you back. Eliminate mental and physical clutter in your life to allow you to focus more time on getting things accomplished or spending time on more pleasant things.

130

Brush your hair with a real-bristle hairbrush 50 to 100 times each night before bed. The brushing stimulates growth and makes your hair more shiny.

131

Tackle stress by signing up for a weekly yoga class. And go to it.

132

Take care of yourself

Your body, mind and soul need regular maintenance and fuelling to run smoothly. Regular doses of exercise and good food rejuvenate and energize you. If you are calm and at peace, you are in better condition to be productive.

133

Herbal conditioning oil

½ cup dried camomile flowers
¼ cup dried rosemary leaves
1 cup safflower or sunflower oil

Place the herbs in the top of a double boiler and add the oil. Heat for 30 minutes. Pour the mixture into a jar. Cover with a piece of muslin secured with a rubber band. Let this stand in a warm place for about a week, stirring it each day. Strain the oil into a clean jar.

To use: warm about ½ cup of the oil – less if your hair is shorter – over a very low heat for a few minutes. Rinse your hair with hot water and squeeze out any excess with your hands. Rub the warm oil into your hair and scalp. Cover with a shower cap, then a warm damp towel. Condition for 20 to 30 minutes then shampoo to remove the oil.

✣ ✣ ✣

134

Focus on being rather than doing

If you rush through life you avoid being yourself. Give yourself time to reflect and experience your feelings. When you experience your feelings, you save time and energy by addressing the underlying issue right away.

135

You should be able to be happy alone. Learn to just be with yourself. When you have time to breathe and reflect you are better able to process the information and ideas that surface.

136

Pick a day and spend it hooking up with an old friend. Even just a long telephone conversation can bring you back into each other's lives and lift your spirits.

137

Make yourself a "special things" box

We all need a place to keep special things hidden away. Buy or make a box for storing the things that make you feel better, whether it is chocolate, a special skin cream or a scented massage oil.

138

Indulge yourself with some extra-special thick bath towels. They're great for making you feel pampered after your morning shower, especially if you're getting ready for a long, busy work day.

139

For every season keep a list of the things you love to indulge yourself with. As the seasons change promise yourself that you will keep to the list.

140

Buy a bubble-blowing kit and blow some bubbles. Sometimes a great way of releasing stress is to become a kid again, even for a short amount of time.

141

A comforting bath

Use ½ to 1 cup of a combination of
any of the following:
dried mint
dried camomile
dried lavender
dried rosemary
dried rose petals
oatmeal, ground in a blender
dried milk

Don't be afraid to experiment in making this deliciously comforting bath mixture. Perhaps try half a cup of mint, camomile and lavender, but only a small amount of rosemary. Or choose two of the herbs and use one cup of each, plus a cup of dried milk for a soothing milk bath.

✤ ✤ ✤

142

Always be kind to yourself. Don't take life too seriously. Total perfectionism is unrealistic. Everyone makes mistakes.

143

Care for your toenails and cuticles

Cut your toenails in a square shape to prevent ingrown nails. Gently push back cuticles with an orange stick. Never cut your cuticles as they stop bacteria from entering the skin.

144

Tie fresh lavender, thyme, and sage together in a small bundle to hang near your desk or work area, even by the kitchen sink. Fresh herbs are cheap and can lift your mood and make you feel calmer.

145

Take the afternoon off. Decide that everything can wait and get back some time for yourself.

146

For a relatively cheap and instant makeover change your cosmetic colours. Buy a new shade of lipstick.

147

Cream cheese treat

1 teaspoon chopped fresh or dry herbs
(basil, thyme, dill, marjoram, chives, mint, oregano)
8 ounces cream cheese

Flavour plain cream cheese with finely chopped fresh or dried herbs for a delicious treat. Keep the flavoured cheese in a covered container to spread on bagels, crackers or French bread instead of skipping breakfast.

148

Make a promise to yourself to do something different. Find out where your local riding school is and try horse-riding or pony-trekking. It's great for toning buttocks and thighs.

149

Make your own bath bag by cutting a circle of muslin or cheesecloth and placing fresh herbs in the centre with fine oatmeal (ground in blender) or powdered milk. Gather the bundle and tie tightly. Tie the bag underneath the tap while the water is running and allow it to soak in your bath water while you are bathing.

150

When you're feeling a bit low have your own private celebration of You. Your accomplishments and your hard work are worth recognizing.

151

Welcome spring. Whether or not the temperatures are beginning to warm up in your part of the world, take a walk, paying particular attention to the little signs that a new season is on its way.

152

In summer, get yourself a great tan. Go to a spray-tanning salon or buy a fake-tanning product and bronze yourself into glamour. For the sake of your skin always use a fake tan.

153

Take five minutes out and let a piece of your favourite chocolate dissolve in your mouth. Bask in the luxury. Finish the whole bar that way.

154

Pick up your spirits. Give yourself permission to focus only on those relationships that truly support and nourish you, at least for a while. You'll feel better for it.

155

Kiwi-banana-strawberry shake

1 medium banana
¼ cup chopped kiwi fruit
⅓ cup chopped strawberries
¼ cup apple juice
¼ cup chopped ice

Indulge in this delicious shake. Combine all the ingredients in a blender and purée until smooth.

Makes one serving.

156

Pamper your creative senses today. Take your camera out with you. Look for interesting or unusual moments you can capture on film.

157

Create your own coffee bar in your kitchen. Purchase good-quality beans from your favourite coffee shop or deli. Add a few flavoured syrups, whipped cream and tasty cookies if you like. Then invite over a few friends.

158

Decide that you are going to be your own best friend. Tell yourself how much you like yourself and why.

159

If the weather is nice pack a picnic full of delicious organic and healthful goodies and go to the nearest beauty spot for lunch.

160

Basic yoga

Relax with this basic yoga exercise. Do not try to stretch further than is comfortable. You may need to bend your knee, but try not to. With practice, you will be able to place your head on your leg, which is the desired goal.

1. Sit with both legs and the palms of your hands (placed at your sides) flat on the floor, with your back straight.
2. Bend one leg at the knee so that it is comfortably touching the inside of the straight leg.
3. Slowly stretch both arms above your head, palms up.
4. Now slowly bend forward at the waist, bringing your head down towards your leg, stretching until your head touches your straight leg.
5. Repeat the movement from step one using the opposite side.

161

For a healthy glow enjoy the fresh air by walking or riding a bicycle and taking a trip out all by yourself.

162

Buy something small that makes you feel cherished such as fresh blackberries, home-made soap or a silk pillowcase.

163

Tropical shake

½ cup diced pineapple
¼ cup diced mango
¼ cup pure apple juice
2 tablespoons low-fat coconut milk
2 tablespoons pure orange juice

Experience relaxation Caribbean-style with this delicious tropical shake. Combine all the ingredients in a blender and purée. Makes one 10-ounce shake.

164

Indulge your curiosity

Go online and expand your mind. The internet offers a world of opportunities. Your local public library should be able to help if you're not connected at home.

165

Do something special just for you

Be as thoughtful in planning your special time as you would be planning special time with your partner or best friend. Then completely bask in the delight of positive self-care. Take especially good care of yourself.

166

On a sunny afternoon host an outdoor tea party with your friends, your children or your friends and their children.

167

Give yourself a cheek massage

Starting at the side of your nose, using your middle and fourth fingers, gently glide your hands over your cheekbones in small circular movements ending at the temples. Try to actually move the skin and muscles around over the bones. Finish by sweeping your hands down your nose and across your lower cheeks.

168

To keep hands soft as silk try a twice-weekly treatment of a mixture of sugar and hand cream. Just mix the ingredients and leave on overnight.

169

Light some scented candles, switch off the lights and sit down to relax in the soothing ambience you have created for yourself. Many candles are scented, with a practically endless choice of fragrances. The soft light and fragrance are sure to relax your mind, body and spirit.

170

On a windy day go to your local park or piece of open ground and fly a kite. Allow your troubles to soar away from you into the sky.

171

Decide you are going to get in shape. Join an exercise group or local gym for good health and good company.

172

For sleek, glossy hair, condition your hair after every wash to make it easy to comb and style. Apply a conditioner with UV protectors if you spend a lot of time outdoors.

173

Set up a table outside in your garden or on your balcony. Invite your partner or your friends to dine with you. Use the best china, light a few candles, and enjoy a glass of wine. Put a vase of freshly cut flowers on the table.

174

Honey-lemon facial

½ teaspoon lemon juice
2 tablespoons honey

Blend the lemon juice and the honey together and spread the mixture over your entire face. Leave on for 15 to 20 minutes, then rinse with warm water and gently pat dry with a soft towel.

175

Give yourself a day off. Sit on a park bench. Just sit there and do absolutely nothing.

176

Choose a scented candle or essential oil with an energizing, spring scent: lemon, basil, bergamot, sweet orange, peppermint, eucalyptus, tangerine, or any floral blend. This will lift your spirits.

177

Refrigerate your favourite body spray, or make your own by adding a few drops of your favourite essential oil to a water spray. Spray the cool mist on your face, the back of your neck, and the soles of your feet after exercise or whenever you feel hot.

178

Soothing foot scrub

½ cup Epsom salts
½ cup baking soda
½ cup table salt
½ cup water
a few drops of your favourite essential oil

Combine equal parts of the above ingredients and add a few drops of your favourite essential oil. Rub the mixture into your feet, sloughing away the rough spots. Finish off by applying moisturizer.

179

Visit a botanic garden and indulge your senses with the aroma of the herbs and flowers.

180

Treat yourself with a high-energy and vitamin-packed home-made fruit smoothie. Blend low-fat yoghurt with your favourite fruit. Serve in an elegant wine glass or goblet to make it feel extra special.

181

If you're bored with your look or haven't changed it for years, get yourself a beauty makeover at your local department store cosmetic counter.

182

Try something you thought you would never do. The sense of achievement you feel will raise your self-esteem and you will feel good about yourself for a long time afterwards.

183

Put together a manicure or pedicure basket. Gather your favourite nail-care products into a basket and keep it handy for full treatments and quick polish changes.

184

Make your kitchen smell welcoming in winter. The smell of seasonal vegetables and fruits, such as pumpkins, sweet potatoes, broccoli, carrots, mushrooms, apples, pears and plums create a warming, welcoming aroma.

185

Stop worrying and pamper your mind. Become aware of the present moment. Turn your attention to the way the sun feels on your face, the way your scalp feels when your hair blows in the wind, the way your children talk and the joy of spending time with your family.

186

Herbal hair rinse

2 cups boiling water
2 tablespoons dried rosemary

Use this quick and easy recipe to make a home-made herbal hair rinse. Pour the boiling water over the dried rosemary. Steep for 15 minutes, strain and rinse your hair with the water.

187

Skin-care from within

Start looking after your hair from within. Vitamin A is a fat-soluble nutrient that is necessary for the maintenance and healing of epithelial tissues. Your skin is of course your largest expanse of epithelial tissue. Eggs, oysters and low-fat dairy products are all rich in vitamin A.

188

Have a great big bowl of your favourite ice cream. Add whipped cream for extra indulgence.

189

The joy you seek in life can be found in living every day to its fullest. It's the little things that we often gloss over that mean the most in our lives if we take the time to notice them. Make the effort to be fully present and experience the moments in each day.

190

A tummy-toning exercise

This tummy-toner can be done while sitting at your desk. Sit in an upright position on your chair, tighten your abdominal muscles and breathe in. Hold this position for ten seconds. Breathe out and release the abdominal muscles. Repeat this exercise 30 times.

191

For a sense of complete well-being make sure that you get at least seven hours of sleep every night. Anything less will leave you tired and irritable and feeling under the weather.

192

Honey and cream facial for dry skin

1 teaspoon honey
2 tablespoons heavy whipping cream

Combine the honey and the cream. Beat together and pat the mixture on to your face, rubbing gently and smoothing your skin as you do this. Leave on for a few minutes, then rinse gently with warm water.

193

Lighten up yourself and others

Why not laugh? You don't have to be serious all the time. Have a really good laugh – it feels good.

194

Appreciate the beauty of nature all around you. Whether you focus on the stars above, the distant hills, or the tree in your garden, it is a great health boost to feel good about enjoying life.

195

Light candles in your house every evening to create a special mood around you. Don't save them just for special occasions.

196

Firm up your skin

Vitamin C is necessary for firm skin, as it helps to maintain collagen, the underlying support structure of the skin. It also protects your skin from damage from the environment. Citrus fruits, tomatoes and berries are all rich in vitamin C.

197

A great pick-me-up is to have a foot massage and a pedicure. If you make your feet feel good you will feel good all over.

198

Home-made room freshener

Equal quantities of:
dried lavender
dried rosemary
ground cloves
ground cinnamon
baking soda

Make your home smell gorgeous with this home-made room freshener. Combine the above ingredients and sprinkle on your carpet. Leave for one hour, then vacuum. If you have a very light-coloured carpet be sure to test a small area first.

199

Nothing beats a face-mask for an instant beauty pick-me-up. Select one to suit your skin type then put your feet up as it takes effect. Relax and collect your thoughts.

200

Take turns with your friends to host home-spa days for pampering yourselves. Choose different themes and treatments for each other. Being pampered means different things to different people so choose what feels good for you.

201

In cold weather mix a bit of petroleum jelly with honey and apply to your lips twice a week to prevent chapping.

202

Special body treat

1 teaspoon ground, dried fruit peel
3 teaspoons ground almonds
2 teaspoons oatmeal
1 pinch clove powder
1 teaspoon crushed, dried rose petals
1 pinch nutmeg powder
2 tablespoons almond oil
2 drops neroli (or a citrus oil)
2 drops sandalwood (or patchouli)

Create a paste by blending the ingredients. Spread the paste over your entire body, focusing especially on drier areas. Massage the paste in and wipe off any excess with a dry cloth.

203

Foot scrub

Banish dead skin and calluses. Massage an exfoliating body scrub into the bottoms of your feet. Leave the scrub on, and use a pumice stone to buff down calluses and smooth away dead skin cells. Rinse your feet with cool water.

204

If you've had a hard day at work or just need to unwind, put on some relaxing music, light a few scented candles and run yourself a warm bath. Decide to ignore or switch off the phone while you are in the bath. Don't bother with scrubbing and cleaning – simply lie back and relax.

205

Dry skin face-mask

½ a banana
1 tablespoon honey
2 tablespoons sour cream

Pamper your skin with this home-made face mask for dry skin. Apply the mixture to your face and allow to set for about ten minutes. Gently wipe off with a damp washcloth.

206

Almond meal mask

25 almonds, finely ground
1 tablespoon of aloe gel
a few drops of sesame oil
1 cup milk or warm water

Mix the almond meal with the aloe gel. Add the sesame oil and mix until the ingredients are thoroughly blended. Dampen your face slightly with milk or warm water. Apply the mask and leave on for 15 minutes. Rinse off with warm water.

207

In order for bath salts to be most effective you must relax for at least eight minutes in the bath. Slowly stand up to prevent light-headedness and rinse off under the shower.

208

Banish blackheads

Equal quantities of:
baking soda
water

Mix the baking soda and water in your hand and use the mixture to gently scrub the problem area for two to three minutes. Rinse off with warm water.

209

If you have tried lots if diets and haven't found any of them successful perhaps you need to change your thinking. Don't think "diet", think about smarter, healthier eating. You will lose weight, look better and feel better.

210

For a self-massage, mix two to three drops of essential oils in a tablespoon of sweet almond oil. Warm the mixture between your hands and apply to your skin with light, stroking motions all over your body, always moving in the direction of the heart. Wait at least 15 minutes before rinsing off to allow the oils to sink into your skin for a deeply moisturizing treatment.

211

If you want glowing skin, make sure you drink the recommended eight glasses of water a day. You will notice a difference in your skin because you are keeping it hydrated from the inside.

212

Summer fruit facial

a handful of strawberries
a fresh nectarine
a fresh papaya
1 egg white
½ an English cucumber

Purée all the ingredients in a blender and apply the mixture to your face. Relax for 15 minutes. If you experience any stinging sensation, remove the mask immediately.

213

If you're feeling a bit pale and uninteresting, get a fake tan. A tanned body always looks leaner than a white one. Don't go for the real thing though – a fake tan is much kinder to your skin.

214

Citrus fragrances are known to have refreshing and re-energizing properties. For an early morning start, soak your sleepiness away with tangy, fruit-scented shower gels.

215

If you want to feel elegantly dressed in special clothes make them smell special. Empty the drawers of your dresser and line them with scented liner paper to make your clothes smell gorgeous.

216

Enjoy some delicious, expensive chocolate. Contrary to popular belief, chocolate is best enjoyed alone. Close your mind to all else, and savour every mouthful. From the first taste, the slow melting in the heat of your mouth, the satisfaction of your taste buds, to the slow dripping down your throat.

217

If you're feeling super-stressed, tell yourself that it is all right to take a little time out to recoup your energy levels. Ignore the telephone, fax, email and doorbell for at least half a day.

218

You can enjoy being alone. Don't read, don't talk and don't think. Just feel. Give your whole being over to the enjoyment of solitude.

219

Before you shower or bath, use a dry loofah to brush your whole body. Use long sweeping strokes over your whole body towards your heart. Follow this with a relaxing bath or shower and moisturize afterwards. Certain scents like vanilla, lavender, cucumber and green apple have been proved to increase relaxing alpha waves in the brain.

220

Take good care of your body. Eat and drink sensibly. Overdoing alcohol and food may seem to benefit you at the time, but only leads to feeling bad in the long run.

221

Have an image makeover

You want to look good, whatever form that takes for you. Stop doing the same things you've always done with your appearance such as styling your hair in a certain way. Do something you thought you'd never try. Take the time to experiment. You never know, the new thing that you try might just look fantastic.

222

Try to make time in your life for doing something relaxing every day. It could be yoga or meditation or it could be a new hobby like gardening or painting.

223

A soothing bath-time soak for winter

½ cup oatmeal or bran
a small silk or cotton cloth

Moistureless winter air can leave your skin feeling rough and flaky. Both oatmeal and bran have a soothing, hydrating effect. This is a great soothing soak for the bath in winter which will leave your skin feeling smooth and soft. Place the oatmeal or bran in the centre of cloth. Fold and tie the cloth into a pouch and place it in a warm bath.

224

Home-made conditioner

¼ cup olive oil
¼ cup safflower oil
¼ cup honey

Try this home-made conditioner for hair which has been dried by the wind. Combine all the ingredients in a small saucepan and heat until just boiling. Remove immediately from the heat and let it cool. Pour the mixture into a plastic spray bottle and spray on the ends of hair while wet. Wrap a warm, wet towel around your hair and leave it in place for one hour. Shampoo the mixture out of your hair, rinse and dry as usual. The mixture should be stored in a cool place.

225

Release your inner beauty. For inner peace that will shine through in your face, develop a forgiving attitude to others. Let other people do their own thing, whatever that may be.

226

If you always feel rushed and stressed your appearance will suffer. You will be able to see it in your skin and hair. Ask for help when it's needed, set priorities, pace yourself and take time out for yourself.

227

You will look and feel better if you get at least seven hours of sleep at night. Make sure that you get enough sleep to give your body and mind enough time to relax and rejuvenate.

228

A facial smoothie

3 tablespoons yoghurt
3 large strawberries

Blend the yoghurt and strawberries. Apply the mixture to your face and relax for ten minutes. The yoghurt cleans and nourishes and the strawberries help to exfoliate dead skin cells.

229

An eye massage

Put some eye cream on the tip of your fourth finger. Apply it with a light tapping motion around your eyes starting at the outer corners, under your eyes, pressing the points between your eyes, on either side of your nose with your finger while counting to 30. Continue over your lids, finishing off with gentle pressure on your temples.

230

Pamper your mind by developing your sense of history. Visit your local library for information about self-guided tours and local history. Take a historic walking tour of your town or city.

231

You deserve some peace and quiet. Turn off the phone and the television, close your eyes and revel in the stillness. Or if you would rather not have peace and quiet, turn on your stereo and listen to your favourite music drifting out of the speakers

232

An anti-double-chin massage

This chin and neck massage will help you to avoid developing a double chin. Using your middle and index fingers, massage your chin, using small anticlockwise circular movements, moving up to your ears. Repeat three times then gently slide your hands down your neck with a kneading motion.

233

Everyone feels special and pampered if they get a treat once in a while. Spend on a luxury item for yourself, a cashmere sweater, for example, or silk underwear or sexy shoes.

234

Camomile eye compress

2 camomile teabags
1 cup hot water

Use these camomile eye compresses to get rid of puffiness and dark circles around your eyes. Soak the teabags in the hot water. Drain the excess water and place the teabags in the refrigerator. Place the bags over your eyes for about five minutes or until the bags warm to room temperature.

235

Eight steps to the perfect bath

Treat yourself to the perfect bath as relief for an aching mind, body and soul by following the steps outlined below.

1. Make sure the water is warm, but not too hot. Water that is too hot can dry the skin.
2. Fill the bath ¾ full to make sure that it covers you.
3. Add your favourite bath oil, or a few sprigs of rosemary or lemon oil.
4. Play some of your favourite music.
5. Have ready a gentle scrub that you can use all over your body. A terry washcloth with almond oil is perfect. Remember that just a little almond oil will go a long way.
7. Light some scented candles to create a relaxing mood.
8. Have a big, fluffy towel waiting for you when you get out.

236

Liking yourself will shine through and your face will glow. Learn to love yourself for who you are. If you like and accept yourself, those around you will too.

237

A natural shine-enhancer for your hair

1 pumpkin
1 egg
1 cup natural yoghurt

Use this natural shine-enhancer to treat your hair. Scoop out the inside of the pumpkin and mix it with the egg and the yoghurt. The pumpkin will clarify your hair, while the egg adds shine. Leave the mixture on for 15–20 minutes. Then rinse your hair with very cool water. This treatment will give your hair exceptional shine.

238

Make sure that you smell nice. We can't control everything in our lives but we can control how we smell. If you know you smell gorgeous you will feel gorgeous.

239

The contents of your kitchen cupboards and fridge have all the ingredients for a great facial. Experiment – make up your own! Here are some guidelines.

For normal skin, use natural, organic yoghurt or honey.

For normal-to-dry skin, mix together two to three teaspoons of organic bran with one teaspoon of olive oil and one egg yolk.

For sensitive skin, mix just a teaspoon of baking soda with water, and rub in circular motions on to damp skin.

240

If you have tried your best to look great and people tell you that you look good, you have achieved something. Be kind to yourself – accept compliments gracefully.

241

Sometimes it is important to accept that you have the right to pamper yourself. It is okay to say, "This is just for me."

242

A facial steam bath

Give yourself a facial steam bath by holding your face above a bowl filled with boiling water for 15 minutes. Add a few drops of camomile oil to soothe, or a couple of teabags, or lavender, which acts as a mild antiseptic, to the water. Drape a large bath towel over your head and set a timer. When the 15 minutes are up, rinse with cold water to close the pores, or clean and close the pores with a little witch hazel.

243

A bottom-shaping exercise

This is a great exercise for getting your bottom in shape.

1. Stand with your legs shoulder-width apart.
2. Rest your hands lightly against a surface that is at about chest level.
3. Extend one leg sideways, keeping it straight.
4. Hold the position for about five seconds.
5. Now slowly bring your leg back to the starting position.
6. Keep doing the exercise, alternating legs.

244

A great way of grabbing some "me" time is to read a great book. Lose yourself in an absorbing story.

245

A herbal soak

Add herbs to your bath for a pampering soak. You can add them directly to the bath water, or put them into a muslin bag and tie it directly under the tap as the water is running. You could also add scented oil to the mixture if you like. Useful herbs are:

camomile – soothing and cleansing
comfrey – rejuvenating
lovage – deodorizing and cleansing
lady's mantle – soothes skin irritation
black tea – relieves sunburn
mint – soothing and relaxing
lavender – relaxing and aromatic

246

If you have a day when you feel you have too much to do, don't make yourself overwrought and stressed. Prioritize – do the things that are important first. Remember that you can only do one thing at a time. Trying to do more than one thing at a time will only put extra stress on you.

247

Pets are wonderful things. They are affectionate, make you feel wanted and lower your blood pressure into the bargain! Spend time with your pets – you will be surprised how relaxed they can make you feel.

248

Orange cornmeal mask

1 orange, peeled
½–1 cup cornmeal
½ cup uncooked oatmeal

On a rainy morning revive your face with this orange cornmeal mask. Put the orange in the blender along with the cornmeal. Add the oatmeal and mix well. Apply the mixture to your slightly damp face. Leave on for ten minutes, then spray a bit of warm water on your face and use a circular motion to work the mask around the face. Remove with warm water.

249

Buy your favourite ice cream and eat as much as you like. Just for today.

250

Get some body into your hair. Towel-dry your hair after your shower and detangle with a vent brush to build body. Apply a volumizing mousse at the roots, lifting sections of your hair as you dry it.

251

Massage foot cream into your feet using long upward strokes, moving from your toes to your calves.

252

Surround yourself with positive family and friends who make you feel good about yourself. Nurture relationships with people who are interested in developing your potential and who are worthy of your trust.

253

Have a "self-love" bath. Buy beautiful candles, scented oils or flowers. Fill the bath tub with water. Play relaxing and sensual music. Slip into the warm water, daydream and allow yourself to bask.

254

Nourishing sleep

Try to get enough sleep. If necessary, have a snooze during the day. Learn relaxation techniques such as picturing yourself lying on a soft, lush lawn bathed in the soft glow of moonlight. Let go … feel a deep sense of peace as you listen to your gentle, even breathing.

255

Bring excitement back into your life. Join a running club or try doing something new like taking music or dancing lessons after work. Dancing is also a fun way of meeting other people and will help you to get into shape.

256

Using herbs, in a bath or in a pouch on your pillow or sofa, is an inexpensive yet elegant way to pamper yourself when you take a few minutes, or ideally a few hours, of quiet time.

257

Take another look at your diet. Experiment with new foods and new recipes. Be sure to include plenty of fruit and vegetables to give you good skin, nails and hair.

258

Try to lower the level of stress in your life. If you have a lot of stress at work, prioritize. Plan your time and draw up a schedule. This will help you to keep track of things that need to be done and when they need to be done by.

259

You are an important and special person and are worth pampering. Remember to make time for yourself even if it is just five minutes. Listen to your favourite CD. It might change your mood.

260

Don't be afraid to treat yourself. If it feels good then do it. Why not? Spoil yourself with any positive experience you can think of. Remember, it should be something you enjoy and done just for you.

261

Spruce up your nails

Apply a base coat and two coats of your favourite polish, followed by a top coat. Let your nails dry for at least half an hour, then rub a dab of oil into your cuticles and nail beds to moisturize them.

262

Look after your skin

Wear sunscreen and don't spend too much time in the sun. Apply a sunscreen with an SPF of at least 15 every day and, in the summer, keep out of the sun between 11 am and 3 pm when the sun's rays are most intense.

263

Be kind to your body. Follow a healthy eating plan. Your daily diet must include essential nutrients and consist of a wide range of foods, but in moderation. Cut down on your intake of hydrogenated fats (found in junk food) and processed meats because these foods increase your risk of heart disease.

264

In order to take care of your family and friends, you need first to take care of yourself.

265

To keep your skin's oil production normal, you should make sure that your diet contains enough B vitamins. These help to convert calories into energy for skin metabolism and are components of the enzymes that maintain normal skin function. The best vitamin B sources are fish, whole grains, peanut butter and eggs.

266

Vitamin E helps to slow the ageing of skin cells by reducing the production of an enzyme called collagenase, which breaks down collagen, leaving your skin sagging and wrinkly. Sun exposure also depletes your skin of vitamin E, making it more vulnerable to sun damage. The best sources of this antioxidant are salmon, legumes, extra-lean meat, leafy vegetables and olive and sesame oil.

267

A great way of grabbing some "me" time is to read a great book. Lose yourself in an absorbing story.

268

Get out of the house and into the fresh air. Walk for 15 minutes with no destination. Whether you go alone or with someone, just make sure you're outside (no treadmills will do for this!). As you walk, be on the lookout for signs of nature.

269

To make an energizing body scrub, add grapefruit oil to a loofah or body brush

270

Life cleaning

Tidying your house can be very therapeutic. It can clear your head and help you to make sense of your life. Start with one drawer, then progress to a cupboard. After that, a whole room. Give anything of value that you don't need any more to charity. Put everything else in big black garbage bags and throw them away.

271

If you have overindulged the night before, help your liver to cope with all the toxins from your wild night out by taking some milk thistle tincture (available from health shops). Also take a vitamin B complex to help protect your body and liver against the toxins.

272

Herbal baths

Fresh or dried herbs can be used for a relaxing bath. Use herbs such as lavender, rosemary, lemon verbena or lemon balm. To infuse the herbs combine four cups of boiling water with four tablespoons of herbs. Steep for 30 minutes, strain and add the liquid to your bath.

273

You already have some things in your life that you should feel great about. Make a list of things that excite you, however big, small, likely or unlikely, then make them happen. Appreciate what you have – your child's hug or a good book. Learn new skills, devote yourself to a new cause, make new friends, but be realistic – accept that we are all better at some things than at others.

274

Get yourself a box of biscuits or a bowl of popcorn, a glass of cold juice or a mug of hot chocolate and a book or some magazines. Lie in bed and read and eat. Have a very peaceful afternoon.

275

Oatmeal face scrub

Add just enough warm water to loose oatmeal to form a paste and then massage the mixture into your skin for a quick exfoliating facial. Rinse off and your skin will be soft and fresh – free of dead skin cells.

276

You must be able to laugh at yourself if you want to live a happy and serene life. It's impossible to laugh and be angry at the same time. People who laugh a lot don't usually get ulcers.

277

One week detox

Drink at least eight 8-ounce glasses of distilled water each day. Eat only raw fruit and vegetables for the first two days. On the third to the seventh day you may introduce some cooked vegetables and lean meat such as chicken or fish. Avoid all dairy and wheat products for the duration of the detox.

278

Expand your horizons

Be creative. Give life to your dream, be it a painting, a tasty meal, a dress, an invention or a business plan. Get active with worthwhile activities at work, within the family and the community.

279

Keep your hair clean and shiny but beware of overdoing it. Shampoo every other day, or less frequently if possible. Excess shampooing strips the natural oils from your hair and can make it dry and damaged.

280

For a mid-morning snack, eat something like a wholewheat bread roll thinly spread with cottage cheese and a piece of fruit. Eating healthy snacks will stimulate your metabolism and keep your blood sugar levels steady until lunchtime.

281

Have something that you can refer to whenever you feel a bit low. It could be a favourite book of poems or you could even put something together yourself. Purchase a blank notebook or journal and write inspirational quotations and sayings to read and review later.

282

An extra-special skin treatment tailored to your specific complexion type is a great boost. Dry skin must be moisturized and lubricated; combination skin needs scrupulous cleansing and refining; normal skin must be treasured and preserved. Don't forget the rules for applying cream: use both hands and stroke with an upward motion from chin to ears, from brow to temples, from the inner corner of each eye across the upper lids and then from the outer corners along the lower lids. Follow the same movements when removing cream with tissues or cotton wool.

283

Gentle facial cleanser for normal skin

½ cup oatmeal or cornmeal
plain yoghurt (enough to make a paste with the oatmeal)

Mix the oatmeal and the yoghurt together. Smooth over the entire face, avoiding the eye area. Wash off with warm water.

284

For a spoil-yourself snack, choose almonds, pecans and walnuts, eating them individually and slowly.

285

Sharing things will often leave you feeling lighter-hearted. Spend some time with your friends and/or partner to talk, laugh and listen.

286

Before going to bed apply a small amount of cleanser all over your face, massaging in circular movements. Put a muslin cloth in hot water, wring it out and hold it over your face until it cools. Repeat this three times to warm and soften your skin to make exfoliation easier. Now wrap the muslin around your hand and gently rub (exfoliate) your skin using firm circular movements, until all the cleanser has been removed. Place the cloth in cold water, wring it out and hold over your face to tighten your pores. Next morning, put the muslin in warm water and wring it out before wiping your face with it. Finish with a cold cloth to tighten your pores.

287

Wash your face twice a day with a face wash that suits your skin type. Use an organic cosmetic sponge to remove the wash from your face – rinsing alone doesn't get rid of all the dirt and dead skin cells.

288

Lavender-vinegar hair rinse

Half fill a jar with lavender leaves and flowers. Top it up with white vinegar and seal it with a plastic lid, or put some plastic wrap over the jar first before closing the lid. Store the rinse in a dark place, such as a cupboard, for three to four weeks. Mix one part of your lavender-vinegar to one part distilled water and use to rinse hair after shampooing.

289

Invest in a few meditation tapes. Give yourself some time each day to practise. It will help you relax.

290

If you have been feeling under the weather and know that you have accumulated some bad habits, start improving your life right now. Do one small thing to improve your health. Good health is one of the best ways to pamper yourself.

291

Give yourself a daily head massage. Massage your head daily for for five to ten minutes to promote blood flow to the scalp and so improve the condition of your hair. Starting at your temples, work towards the back of your head, applying pressure in circular motions. Turn your head upside down and give your hair a good brushing from the scalp to the ends, which stimulates the scalp and spreads natural oils through the hair.

292

Take some time to pamper yourself, both inside and out, mentally and physically. After all, as hard as you work, you owe it to yourself to take some time and give yourself a little TLC. Your mind and body will thank you for it.

293

If you want to get rid of flakes and keep your lips soft, use a soft toothbrush and brush gently across your lips. To keep the flakes away apply a moisturizing lip balm regularly.

294

Stress-buster bath

1 cup fresh rose petals
1 cup cider or white-wine vinegar

If tensions are soaring, the answer could be growing in your garden. It's roses to the rescue; their fragrant petals contain relaxing oils. Add cider or white-wine vinegar to moisturize and to restore skin's natural acidity. Place the petals in a clean, screw-top jar. Heat the vinegar to boiling point and pour it over the petals. Cover with a lid and soak for two weeks, occasionally shaking the jar. Then strain the liquid through a sieve lined with a coffee filter or a piece of muslin. Use half a cup of the infusion in a warm bath.

295

Your hair reacts very quickly to a bad diet, often becoming dry and dull or oily and lank. Follow a well-balanced diet rich in proteins and fatty acids to keep your hair healthy-looking.

296

Have a long soak in the bath. Start filling your bath tub with warm water, and then add a capful or two of your best bubble bath or bath foam. The ideal bubble bath or bath foam will contain soothing camomile or lavender ingredients. Camomile and lavender are two of the most popular herbs that are known to relax and calm the human body. To bathe your tired body, there are many different types of scented gels you can use which will make your skin feel soft and supple. Relax in the warm water and feel the tensions of the day just soak away. For added pampering, you could splash on an after-bath tonic, spritz or powder to make you feel fresh.

297

Everyone deserves a holiday now and again. Take some time off work to do exactly what you want to do.

298

Fragrant feet

Mix together baking powder, sage and tea tree oil. Sprinkle on clean, dry feet then dust off the residue. The mixture absorbs sweat and refreshes your feet.

299

Shut out the world. After a hard day at work, come home, put on your warmest, softest bath robe and relax with a glass of wine and your favourite CD.

300

A refreshing facial toner

1 ounce evening primrose oil
3 ounces witch hazel
10 drops grapefruit oil
5 drops tea tree oil
5 drops cypress oil

Combine all the ingredients in a bottle and shake to mix. Use as you would any other facial toner.

301

Whether you live in a house or a flat, make yourself a spring window box. Plant bulbs of daffodils, hyacinths and crocuses and wait for them to bloom.

302

Refresh your skin

½ cucumber
1 tablespoon yoghurt
a handful of strawberries
1 teaspoon honey

Mix all the ingredients in a food processor or blender. Apply the mixture to your face and allow it to dry. Gently wipe off with a damp washcloth.

303

A great time to deeply condition your hair is while you are in the bath. Apply a hair treatment product that is suitable for your hair type to wet hair and wrap your hair under a plastic shower cap. The heat and moisture of the bathroom will help the deep conditioning treatment to work better.

304

Pamper yourself and your lover with aphrodisiac essential oils: angelica, cardamom, cinnamon, clary sage, ginger, jasmine, neroli, patchouli, rose, rosewood, violet and ylang-ylang.

305

Plump up your skin for a special night out by mashing an avocado and applying it to your entire face. Leave to harden for about 20 minutes, then gently wipe off with a damp washcloth.

306

Get or make a skipping rope and skip. Skipping on a daily basis strengthens the heart and also increases bone density. It is no longer just something that children do during playtime. Skip for a few minutes each day to increase your muscular strength.

307

To freshen up oily or combination skin

1½ teaspoons honey
juice of ½ a lemon
1 small carton of natural yoghurt
1 egg white, whipped

Mix the above ingredients, stirring in the egg white last. Apply the mixture to your face and allow it to set. Leave on for about 15 minutes then gently wipe off with a damp washcloth.

308

One day detox

Begin the day with some real fruit juice – though avoid orange juice and tomato juice – and eat some raw fruit. Drink herbal tea throughout the day – camomile, red clover, dandelion or peppermint. Eat whichever raw fruits and vegetables you like for your meals. Drink plenty of water throughout the day.

309

Float down a river in a boat. Just feel the sensation of letting go of all your worries.

310

Make your eyes appear bigger by applying two shades of mascara to your eyelashes and using a white pencil on the inner rims of the lower lids. This will immediately open them up.

311

Put aside a little time every day for yourself – relax with a book in the bath or sit in the garden with the sun on your face. Eat properly, exercise regularly and get enough sleep to look and feel your best.

312

Create a favourite place in the house that is just for you. Surround yourself with your things. Try to find some time every day to do something just for yourself such as listening to music, meditating, reading, watching a television show, or just having some quiet time.

313

Change your appearance a little. If you wear glasses or lenses, try coloured contact lenses or a new style of frame.

314

Go shopping, or even just window-shopping, with a close friend.

315

Create a spa experience in your own bathroom. Use your favourite bath oil or bath salts in your bath water, light some candles and listen to some soft soothing music.

316

Allow yourself an hour a week to spend time on you. Take a stress-busting bath using essential oils to improve your mood. Your whole sense of being will benefit. Start off with a body massage using baby oil while you run the water. Surround the bath with candles and put on some relaxing music.

317

For 15 minutes, go back to bed. If you're having a busy or frantic week, indulge yourself a little. Curl up in the comfort of your sheets and blankets.

318

A yoghurt and walnut facial scrub for all skin types

¼ cup plain yoghurt
¼ cup finely ground walnuts

Blend the yoghurt and the nuts. Wet your face, then gently work the scrub into your skin. Rinse off with warm water.

319

Don't just watch television every evening after work. Visit friends or browse through your favourite magazine. Do the things you never seem to have time for.

320

Fresh flowers will always make you feel special. Buy some for yourself and keep them close by you where you can look at them.

321

Smell nice all day. Wash with a shower gel scented with your favourite fragrance and use it all over your body. Add a scented moisturizer as the next layer to building your fragrance. Then apply your favourite perfume.

322

Be kind to your hair

Let your hair dry naturally whenever possible. Blow-drying can dry out hair and may even damage it. If you use heated rollers or curling tongs, use a protective spray on your hair first. If you're in a hurry and have to blow dry-your hair, use the dryer on its lowest, coolest setting.

323

Groom your eyebrows. It is not necessary to change the shape of your brows, just tidy them up. If you do not have time to pluck your eyebrows, comb you them into place, dab a little bit of moisturizer on a soft toothbrush and gently brush it on your brows.

324

Pamper your sense of responsibility. Know your values and live up to them. The more your actions reflect your beliefs, the better you will feel about yourself.

325

Eat plenty of vitamin E for your skin and hair. Make sure you incorporate this vitamin into your daily diet. Good sources are brown rice, nuts, wheat-germ and leafy green vegetables.

326

You cannot keep working like a horse constantly without a break. Take some time out. To be and do your best, you must take time to refuel and rejuvenate.

327

Spend ten to fifteen minutes dealing with those bags under your eyes. A great short-term trick is to apply cool cucumber slices or cool teabags to the under-eye area to help reduce swelling and soothe tired eyes. Place over the eye area and lie back and relax for about 15 minutes.

328

Take one day and make it completely yours. You can either do nothing or then again you could do lots of things. It should be totally up to you.

329

A rejuvenating aromatic shower

Drizzle up to 5 drops of lemon essential oil on a soft sponge. Rub the sponge gently all over your body in circular motions. This stimulates good blood flow and will make your skin tingle and glow. Lemon may be replaced with black pepper or rosemary oil.

330

Green tea

Chinese people have known about the medicinal benefits of green tea since ancient times. Today, researchers are also learning more about the health benefits of drinking green tea. Research has shown that drinking green tea inhibits the growth of cancer cells, lowers bad LDL cholesterol levels and inhibits the abnormal formation of blood clots.

331

Scented shower gel

4 ounces unscented shower gel
40 drops of your favourite essential oil

Add the essential oil to a small bottle of unscented shower gel and mix well. Use as you would any shower gel.

332

Invite your friends round and make them some children's party food. Be kids for the day, play some games and have some fun. You're bound to spend a lot of time laughing.

333

If you want to improve your health and make your skin glow, get regular aerobic exercise. You should probably aim for about 30 minutes a day, three to five days a week.

334

Shoe deodorizer

4 tablespoons cornstarch
4 tablespoons baking soda
20 drops tea tree oil
10 drops lemon oil
10 drops lavender oil

Mix together all the ingredients to make an effective shoe deodorizer. Sprinkle lightly into shoes in the evenings or at times when the shoes will not be worn for a few hours. Smells will not evaporate overnight but your shoes will smell better with prolonged use.

335

Feel that you can indulge yourself in your own private space. At home you are the ruler in your own little kingdom. Don't feel that you always have to live up to others' expectations.

336

Lotion for dry hands

8 ounces unscented lotion
10 drops patchouli oil
20 drops sandalwood oil
5 drops evening primrose oil (or substitute other essential oils of your choice)

Use your favourite essential oils to make this wonderfully effective lotion for dry hands. Pour the lotion into a bowl, add the essential oils and mix well. Once mixed, pour the lotion back into the bottle. Patchouli, sandalwood and carrot seed oils help with dry skin. Test a new blend on a small patch of skin first to be sure that you are not sensitive to it.

337

Be positive about yourself. Don't build your self-esteem around what other people think of you, some people can be over-critical and negative.

338

Lip balm

Papayas contain exfoliating enzymes to help soften lip lines. Mash about a quarter of a papaya into a nice juicy paste. Apply a generous amount on and around your lips. Relax for about 15 minutes, rinse the papaya off and apply lip balm.

339

Always use crisp cotton sheets on hot summer nights to make yourself feel wonderfully chilled out. In winter pamper yourself with warm flannel sheets and snuggle down on cold nights.

349

Have a slow, quiet day. Have a look around some local bookshops and enjoy a cappuccino and some cake in a lovely cafe.

341

Make yourself feel sexy. Wear your favourite perfume, put on a bathrobe, pour yourself a glass of something, turn down the lights and enjoy.

342

Acknowledge and praise yourself for your good qualities such as your lovely smile, your excellent vocabulary or your loyalty. You will notice that as soon as you treat yourself gently, being nice to others will come easily and improve your whole sense of being.

343

Make yourself smile

Keep a funny-thought book or cartoon you like near your work area. Look at it often. This also works with pictures of your family that you find funny.

344

Drink herbal teas

Green tea and herbal teas are soothing and full of health benefits. Peppermint tea and camomile tea are especially great for a boost and for relaxation respectively.

345

Feel loved and loving. Curl up with your favourite pet for ten minutes.

346

If you want a flawless face, you have to exercise. Although toning, cleansing and moisturizing should be part of your beauty routine, exercise will speed up your circulation and leave a nice glow on your face.

347

Relax with a CD of nature sounds. Immerse yourself in a roomful of soothing natural sounds.

348

Salads are not just diet food. They contain nutrients that are brilliant for your hair, skin and general sense of well-being. Make a great big healthy salad for dinner. Grill chicken, cut in strips, place on a bed of lettuce, and top with your favourite dressing.

349

Book a weekend away with friend. It will pick up your spirits and renew your enthusiasm.

350

Spend a day at a health spa. Have as many treatments as you can afford.

351

Relax your body and mind. Lie on the floor in your room or garden and practise some deep breathing exercises. Consciously relax each part of your body, and let the tension melt away with each breath.

352

Let your feet enjoy the luxury of going without shoes. Mow your lawn and run through the freshly mown grass barefoot. You can also try this in your local park.

353

Join a reading or book club. This will have the double benefit of expanding your mind and making new friends.

354

Pamper yourself with a teatime treat. Make your favourite dessert and eat it with real whipped cream.

355

Visit somewhere you've always meant to see. Plan a trip. You could go alone or with a group.

356

In hot weather, spritz yourself regularly. Carry a refreshing mist with you or leave it by your desk for moments when you need a blast of calm. Make your own spritzer with natural mineral water, rose oil, camomile oil and neroli oil.

357

Go for a long walk along a deserted beach or in an empty stretch of parkland and feel yourself among nature.

358

Remember how special you are every day

For a week, ask people what they like best about you. Each day list each different "best thing" about you to look at when you need cheering up.

359

Plan a day where you do some of the things you may dream about doing during your morning commute to work. Browse the shops. Take a nap in your garden. Watch an afternoon film. It's your day today.

360

To avoid premature wrinkles, try sleeping on your back. Years of sleeping with your face pressed against a pillow can cause wrinkles.

361

Make your home like a pampering spa. Keep a basket of your favourite products in your bathroom. Include your favourite sponges, bath salts and oils, body lotions, powders, perfumes, and conditioning treatments.

362

Make every room relaxing when you want it to be. Invest in some lamps so you can soften the lighting.

363

Keep beautiful fresh plants in your bathroom to feel fresh and energized. Plants love the humidity of a bathroom.

364

For those cold winter mornings, invest in an electric towel warmer. This will give you the comfort of lovely warm towels on those chilly days as you get ready for work.

365

A great anti-wrinkling agent is zinc. This trace mineral helps to maintain your skin's elastin and collagen. It is found in seafood, soya, turkey and mushrooms.